*The mission of the non-profit Monterey Bay Aquarium
is to inspire conservation of the oceans.*

How It All Started

On October 20, 1984, the fish came back to Monterey's historic Cannery Row.

Immense schools of squid swarm into the bay to mate and lay eggs, and often end up in nets to be sold as calamari.

It all started in 1977 when four marine biologists at Stanford University's Hopkins Marine Station in Pacific Grove first proposed an aquarium devoted to Monterey Bay. A group of marine scientists, local residents and members of the David and Lucile Packard Foundation of Los Altos, California, soon formed the non-profit Monterey Bay Aquarium Foundation to pursue the project.

The aquarium stands on the site of the Hovden Cannery and on adjoining cannery and warehouse properties. In the early 1970s, Stanford University purchased the property to protect the shoreline next to its Hopkins Marine Station, then sold it to the aquarium foundation in 1978 for $980,000.

The aquarium's unique exhibit approach showcasing regional marine communities rather than individual species was influenced by Edward F. Ricketts, the marine biologist friend of author John Steinbeck. Ricketts' Pacific Biological Laboratory was right next to the Hovden Cannery on Cannery Row.

At the time, most other aquariums exhibited individual or mixed groups of species from different parts of the world, but not from a specific region like Monterey Bay.

With an original mission to promote awareness of the marine environment, the aquarium set out from the beginning to connect people with their natural surroundings, in the hope they would take the next steps and become active ocean stewards.

A painting by artist Bruce Ariss captures the essence of Cannery Row in its heyday.

Gone but not forgotten, the old Cannery Row lives on in paintings and photographs.

Built two years before this photo was taken in 1918, the Hovden Cannery (the long white building) operated until 1972 and was the last of the canneries to close.

HOVDEN CANNERY

Knut Hovden's cannery was the largest on Cannery Row.

Marine biologist Ed Ricketts influenced the aquarium's exhibit approach.

SARDINE CAPITAL

Monterey was once one of the biggest fishing ports in America, and ranked as the sardine capital of the world.

Hordes of silvery sardines have been making a comeback in the bay.

FISHERY COLLAPSE

The Hovden Cannery closed after the sardine fishery collapsed, and the market for canned squid was too small to support the operation.

Cannery Row's "silver harvest," a quarter of a million tons in 1945, dwindled to almost nothing by 1952.

Building the Aquarium

It took four years to reshape the old cannery to bring Monterey Bay Aquarium to life.

Demolition of the abandoned Hovden Cannery began in 1980, with construction underway by the spring of 1981 through the fall of 1984. Some elements of the original cannery building are preserved in the new structure.

Five years later, planning began for the Outer Bay wing to house first-ever exhibits of the open ocean and deep sea portions of Monterey Bay. Construction started in the winter of 1992, with the grand opening of the Outer Bay galleries on March 2, 1996.

How did all this come to be? Initial construction costs of $55 million were provided through a one-time personal gift from David and Lucile Packard. Construction of the $62 million Outer Bay wing was financed with aquarium earnings and contributions from individuals, businesses and foundations. The self-supporting, non-profit aquarium receives no public funds for operating support.

Operational costs as well as education and research programs are funded with revenues from admission and membership fees, individual donations, business sponsorships, foundation grants, evening admissions, and proceeds from the gift and bookstores and restaurant.

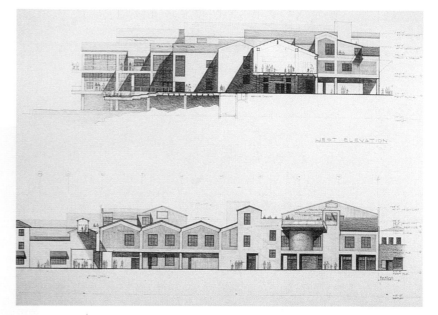

When all the dust had settled, the aquarium covered over three acres, with more than 170,000 square feet of exhibits and public areas, and 26,000 square feet of decks embracing the magnificent ocean views.

Western gulls are one of nine seabird species that breed along the Monterey coast.

Work on the Great Tide Pool had to wait for the lowest of low tides, which occur in the winter and spring.

Millions of pounds of concrete and reinforcing steel and miles and miles of wire and pipe went into the aquarium.

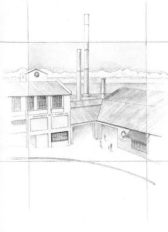

AQUARIUM FOOTPRINT

Extensive behind-the-scenes areas bring the total square footage of the aquarium to more than 300,000.

The ribs of the concrete walls of the giant Outer Bay exhibit support a fiberglass liner. More than two million blue tiles cover the exhibit to create the feeling of looking into the open sea.

CONCRETE AND STEEL

Forty-four million pounds of concrete and 2.8 million pounds of reinforcing steel went into the Outer Bay wing alone.

RIGHT: *The old, rusty Hovden smokestacks were replaced with new ones to retain the look of the original cannery.*

Cannery Row Influence

The buildings give a sense of Cannery Row in its heyday.

The award-winning design of the aquarium preserves the historic flavor of Cannery Row and the old cannery that inspired the aquarium. While elements of the aging Hovden complex were restored for use or display, including the old boilers, pumphouse and warehouse, the majority is new construction.

The architectural firm of Esherick Homsey Dodge and Davis designed both the Ocean's Edge and Outer Bay wings. The design took shape in the hands of specialists who transformed the lines on blueprints into the hard steel, concrete and acrylic of complex seawater systems and giant exhibit tanks.

Embracing the rocky coast, the aquarium was built to withstand 100-year storms, earthquakes, pounding waves and corroding sea water. And as the building was coming to life, exhibits were being created that would bring life to the building.

The Boiler House displays the restored boilers from the old Hovden Cannery, complete with smokestacks, and details the sardine canning process.

What once was Monterey's largest cannery has become a window into the nation's largest marine sanctuary, and the abundance of sea life to be seen there.

Aquarium founders Lucile and David Packard, with Executive Director Julie Packard (middle) on opening day, October 20, 1984.

The aquarium's design is faithful to the look and spirit of historic Cannery Row.

Creating the Exhibits

Each aquarium exhibit holds a living world.

The aquarium exhibits showcase the habitats and sea life of one of the world's richest marine regions.

Creative design and engineering helped create the world's first living kelp forest exhibit, complete with surging swells and moistening salt spray.

Sculptors made the rocks in the exhibits from fiberglass-reinforced concrete (they even made some from molds of real rocks). Years before the aquarium opened, rocks were set out in the bay to be colonized by animals, like sponges and corals and later retrieved.

To give the feeling of peering through a window on the bay, actual wharf pilings were brought from the Monterey Harbor and installed in the Monterey Bay Habitats display.

State-of-the-art technology went into the design and building of the world's largest exhibit of open ocean animals. A company in Japan came up with a new way of making the huge window out of five panels with four almost-invisible seams that withstand the pressure of a million gallons of sea water.

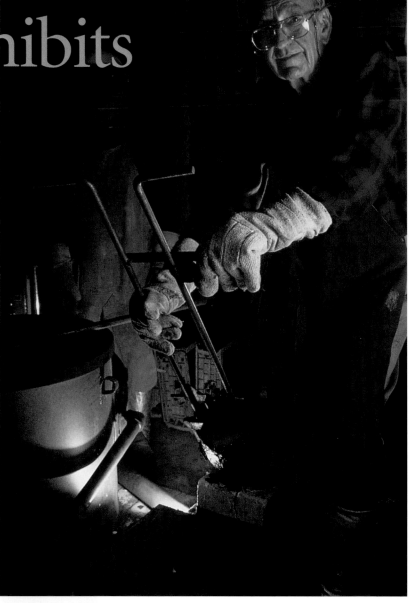

David Packard helped create exhibits at his forge in Big Sur.

Created offsite, lifesize gray whale models made a brief appearance on Cannery Row on their way to the aquarium.

Under repair: A leopard shark circles in the half-empty Kelp Forest exhibit.

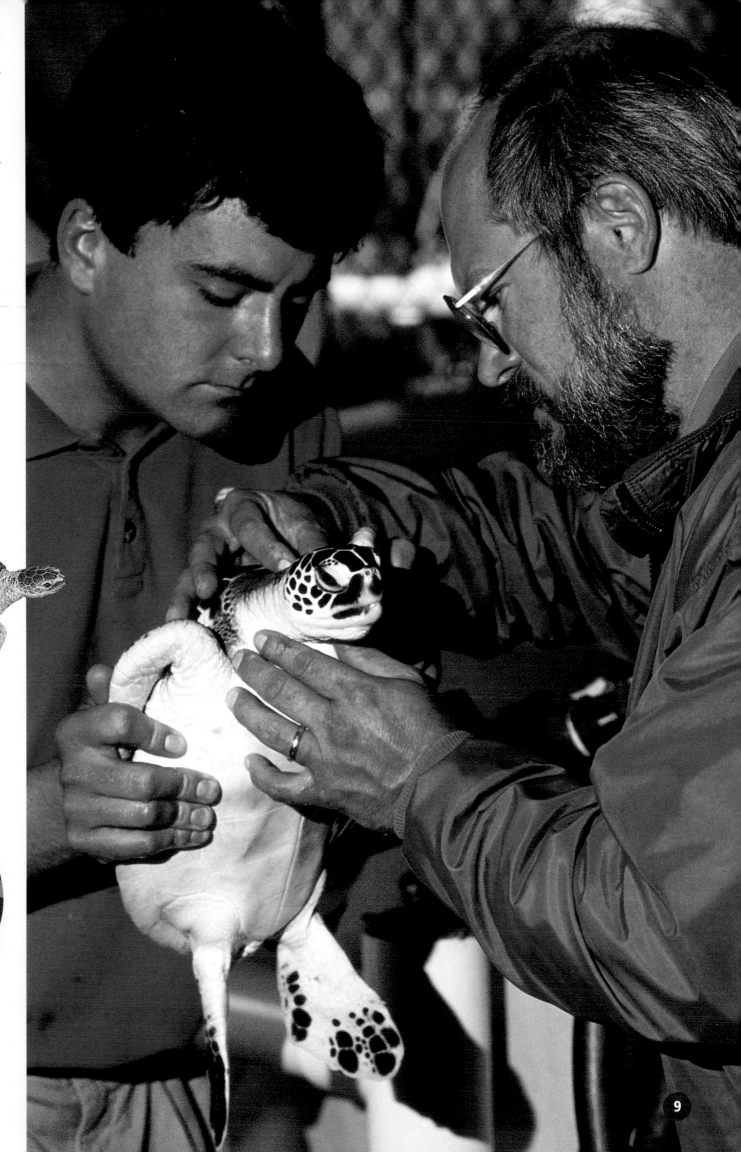

Aquarists raise many of the species you see on exhibit, like the purple-striped, egg-yolk and crystal jellies and sea nettles.

Carefully placing anemones on rocky perches, an aquarist stocks an exhibit.

A sea turtle swims for most of its life, and must come to the surface to breathe air.

Aquarium staff pioneered the husbandry of jellies.

RIGHT: *The aquarium's vet examines a young sea turtle.*

Care and Feeding

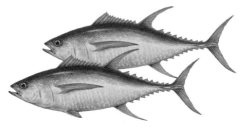

From rearing rescued sea otter pups to feeding a giant octopus, much more happens than meets the eye.

Aquarists maintain order in the little community in each exhibit. They clean and collect, treat and feed, study and stock.

Every day, aquarists feed the animals up to 300 pounds of seafood, groom plants, inspect water lines, siphon out debris and scrub algae off acrylic windows. During these daily rounds, they make sure each animal is healthy and behaving normally. Occasionally, entire exhibits are drained and taken apart for deep cleaning.

Aquarists feed hungry animals more than 92,000 pounds of food a year. To keep smaller and younger animals well fed, gallons of plant and animal plankton are grown for juvenile fishes, small invertebrates and jellies.

Sometimes new animals arrive with bacteria or parasites, and other animals develop infections while on exhibit. When fish get sick, they're treated much the way you'd treat an infected cut, only the animals actually swim in the antibacterial medicine.

Delicate jellies are handfed a rich broth of plankton from a turkey baster.

ABOVE: *To feed a sea turtle, wrap a juicy squid or herring in a large lettuce leaf, and you have a turtle's taco!*

LEFT: *Injured birds are nursed back to health before going on exhibit.*

RIGHT: *What do you feed a hungry octopus? Whole squid, herring, shrimp and, once a week, live crab.*

Behind the Scenes

To make these varied creatures feel at home, fresh sea water, the aquarium's lifeblood, flows through the exhibits.

In the Ocean's Edge galleries, fresh sea water is continuously pumped from the bay. By day, filtering the water leaves it clear for you to see what's inside. At night, unfiltered sea water flows through the exhibits, carrying in the plankton, spores and larvae that sustain animals that filter food from the water. Those spores and plankton that aren't eaten settle and grow in the exhibits.

Water enters through one of two 16-inch-diameter, 980-foot-long intake lines located 55 feet deep in the bay. Pumps draw up to 2,050 gallons of sea water per minute into the aquarium seawater distribution system. Four operating modes permit varying levels of filtration, from raw sea water to sea water cleaned by high-pressure sand filters.

The Outer Bay galleries operate on a "semi-closed" system, bringing in new water rather than relying solely on recirculated water. Sea water from the main intake lines is piped to the new wing where it is heated to 68°F and circulated through the Outer Bay exhibit. Replacement water is added at a rate of 100 gallons per minute. Wastes in the water are removed by biological filters and ozone treatment. A heat recovery system recaptures energy from the water, before any is discharged to the bay.

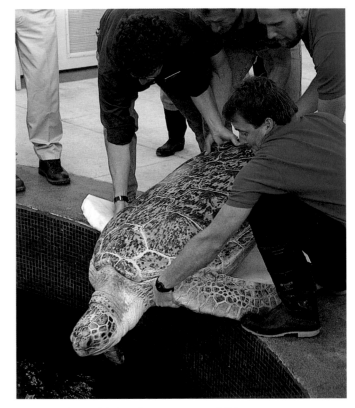

A sea turtle is added to the Outer Bay exhibit.

Computers in the control room monitor the life support systems in the aquarium. Sensors detect critical factors like water level and temperature and microprocessors correct these conditions.

Volunteer divers keep the Kelp Forest exhibit windows free of algae and other settling organisms that come in with the unfiltered sea

Bubbling tubes of algae become food for plankton, which in turn provide a feast for jellies, squid and fishes.

WATER CAPACITY

Nearly three million gallons of sea water swish through the exhibits every day—enough to fill more than 40,000 bathtubs.

Kreisel tanks are circular without corners that could harm jellies.

Giant kelp constantly grow new fronds.

RIGHT: Twice a day, the shorebirds enjoy a banquet of mealworms, waxworms, tubifex worms and krill.

Collecting and Husbandry

Our husbandry staff has a strong commitment to raising marine animals rather than collecting in the wild.

Aquarists successfully culture animals in a highly acclaimed wildlife breeding program that includes more than a dozen marine animals, including Pacific bonito, midshipmen, sailfin sculpin, barracuda and several dozen species of jellies and corals. Many are transferred to other aquariums to help eliminate the need to collect species from the wild.

But when it's necessary to collect, gentle touch and expert methods bring back healthy new residents for the aquarium community. Most of the exhibits mimic the habitats of Monterey Bay, so that's where aquarists go to collect plants and animals.

In deep water and on rocky shores, by line, by net, by trap and by hand, the where and how of collecting varies as widely as the creatures caught. Artificial rocks set in the bay grow thick with marine life before being retrieved by divers and placed in an exhibit. Many deep sea animals are collected by scientists at the Monterey Bay Aquarium Research Institute using a mechanical slurp gun mounted on a remotely operated vehicle.

Spores of seaweeds and the larvae of animals drift in with the sea water, then settle down, carpeting exhibits with changing tapestries of life.

Harmless traps collect spot prawns or deep sea animals like octopuses, crabs, spiny sea urchins and basket stars. Nets gently gather delicate animals like copepods.

New animals arriving at the aquarium don't go on exhibit right away. They get a chance to adjust behind the scenes in a quarantine area until they're healthy and ready to make their debut. It could take as little as a day, or as long as three months.

Thirty-year-old wharf pilings from Monterey Wharf were brought to the aquarium with their rich coating of encrusting animals intact.

An aquarist slowly tows a plankton net through the water, funneling the tiny creatures into a plastic jar at the end.

ABOVE: *Fertilized bonito eggs are collected almost daily from the main Outer Bay exhibit.*

LEFT: *Orange cup corals are the most plentiful animal in the aquarium, numbering more than 90,000.*

RIGHT: *Two-spotted octopuses hatch from eggs at the aquarium.*

Divers carefully collect jellies in water-filled plastic bags to keep from damaging these delicate animals.

The true measure of an aquarium's success is not solely how many people come, but how many leave with a greater awareness of the wealth of life our oceans hold. For only through this awareness will the oceans rise to the forefront of world conservation efforts, where they belong.

— JULIE PACKARD

The Ocean's Edge

Wildness reminds us what it means to be human, what we're connected to rather than what we are separate from.

—TERRY TEMPEST WILLIAMS

Located in the heart of the largest protected marine area in America, Monterey Bay ranks among the world's most diverse and spectacular marine regions. The bay's a patchwork of habitats, from the deep canyon to the wharves jutting from shore. The diversity of sea life found here is breathtaking, thanks to currents that carry cold, nutrient-rich water into the bay—an upwelling that forms the base of an intricate food web.

The aquarium's permanent exhibits focus on our close connection to the rich and varied life of these marine habitats in the Monterey Bay National Marine Sanctuary. It's all laid out on a Habitats Path that lets you explore and experience sea life in natural habitats, from the wave-tossed Ocean's Edge to the mysterious Outer Bay, and beyond.

In 2005, a dramatic transformation of the original exhibit galleries opened. "The Ocean's Edge: Coastal Habitats of Monterey Bay" features new experiences that include a visit to an octopus's den, a walk beneath crashing waves, and a stroll amid shorebirds and gliding bat rays. Throughout the exhibits, visitors discover ways to get personally involved in ocean conservation.

The new exhibits and galleries inspire, engage and empower us to protect wildlife and wild places now and for the future.

The new Ocean's Edge galleries "put people in the picture" by sharing not only the nearshore habitats and creatures, but also how people interact with them.

For more about the bay and the Monterey Bay National Marine Sanctuary, visit www.montereybayaquarium.org or pick up the aquarium's *Field Guide to the Monterey Bay Aquarium.*

The aquarium is as close as most people will ever get to exploring the wilderness that lies just beyond its decks.

Kelp Forest

Off the coast beyond the pounding breakers, where light speckles the seafloor, grow the giant kelp.

One grove of giant kelp stands apart. The Kelp Forest exhibit, an aquarium centerpiece, looks so natural you may think you're looking through a window to the bay.

Sardines, leopard sharks, sheephead and a host of other fishes weave among the fronds of kelp, just as they do in the wild. The exhibit, oriented to the sunlight, opens to the sky, and the light streaming through the amber fronds helps the kelp grow.

Pumps push more than 4,000 gallons of sea water a minute through jets placed to generate natural currents in the exhibit. And the kelp here sways in a surge—vital to the plants—created by a special wave machine. Combined with water jets hidden in the exhibit's rockwork walls, the surge maintains the constant water motion the kelp requires to absorb enough nutrients.

Like the wild kelp forests, the exhibit changes with each passing season, growing in the spring and dying back in the winter.

At 28 feet high, the Kelp Forest is one of the tallest aquarium exhibits in the world, and the first living kelp forest community ever created at an aquarium. You can view the Kelp Forest on the first and second floors, and through third-floor viewing windows that look out onto the top of the kelp canopy.

A garibaldi is a rare sight as far north as Monterey Bay.

ABOVE: *Sea lions and other wildlife feast on the rich assortment of creatures living in the kelp forest. Old fishing line and plastic sixpack rings are deadly traps for these animals.*

LEFT: *Sardines swirl through the kelp fronds in a school that moves like one large fish.*

For more about kelp forests, visit our web site www.montereybayaquarium.org.

GIANT KELP

Kelp grows up to six inches per day out in the bay, and at nearly the same rate in the exhibit.

Strawberry anemones carpet the kelp forest floor.

Like most sharks, leopard sharks reproduce slowly and are vulnerable to overfishing.

A surge machine is a key to this remarkable experiment in keeping kelp alive in an aquarium.

RIGHT: *The Kelp Forest exhibit holds 335,000 gallons of sea water, and its largest acrylic windows are 7¼ inches thick.*

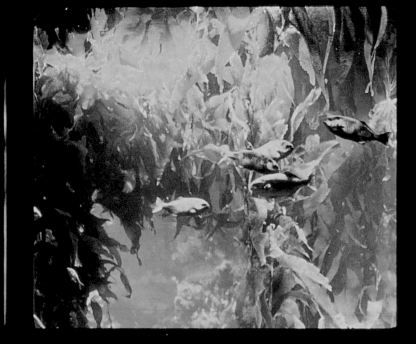
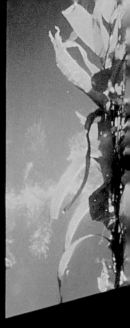

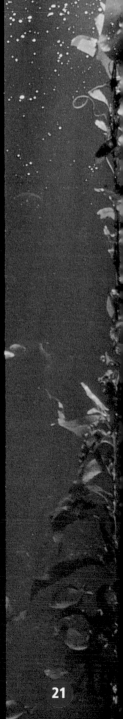

Kelp Lab

It formed a seaweed carpet . . . red, brown and green algae, different shapes and kinds.

While the three-story Kelp Forest exhibit presents a towering forest of the California coast's giant kelp, the Kelp Forest gallery on the second floor reveals more intimate landscapes. Hundreds find homes here, in every nook and cranny.

Thickets of seaweeds carpet the rocks in a constant battle for space. Camouflaged kelpfishes nestle among the low-lying red algae, wizards at remaining unseen. Abalones tuck out of site in cracks and crevices. The sand channel exhibit uses mirrors to create an illusion of spaciousness.

The Kelp Lab, where gentle touching is encouraged, ventures even deeper into the forest. Feel the bumpy turkish towel seaweed or a feather boa kelp. Or try to find the decorator crab in its clever disguise. Digital microcopes reveal the tiniest of the hidden jewels that live here.

A kelp crab's many legs help it hold fast to a swaying giant kelp.

Schools of anchovies swim in tight silvery balls for protection from predators.

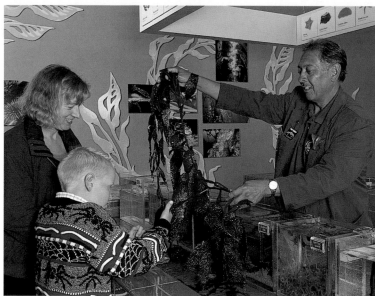

ABOVE: *Aquarium guides, trained to interpret marine life, encourage a sense of wonder and discovery.*

RIGHT: *Brittle stars tuck in tight in the tangled holdfasts anchoring kelp to the seafloor.*

Melibes give off a scent of water-melon, but we don't know why.

Strawberry anemones wage silent turf wars with other colonies, jabbing harpoons at each other. Slightly different shades of pink give away the boundaries.

KELP FRONDS

Kelp fronds get torn up in the waves, and may last only six months, but kelp are constantly growing new ones.

Giant kelp creates forests as productive as rain forests on land, or coral reefs in tropical seas.

RIGHT: *A sarcastic fringehead protects its home, and will even nip at a curious diver who peers too close.*

Deep Reef

I'd like to be under the sea
In an octopus's garden in the shade

–RINGO STARR

In the bay, a deep reef looms over the sandy seafloor in cold, quiet waters hundreds of feet deep. Animals flourish in this sunless sea. Some blanket the reef in living color; others spend their dark days hunting and hiding—lurking in caves or retreating into the shadows.

Hiding in the recesses of the Deep Reef gallery, a jumble of rocks harbors two Pacific giant octopuses. Look carefully. They're masters of disguise, changing skin texture and color to blend in with their surroundings. Even a fully grown, 30-foot, 600-pound octopus can be hard to find in the wild if it doesn't want to be seen.

Nearby, a sheep crab rests by day and forages for food at night. On the reef, it eats anything it can scavenge, like the remains of fishes and other creatures.

Watching and waiting, large wolf-eels and lingcod keep quiet in hopes that prey will stray too near. Their skeletons on exhibit reveal powerful, toothy jaws that mean business.

Hovering over the reef, clusters of red rockfishes almost disappear in the dark waters. Most grow slowly and live a long time. In fact, several species live more than 100 years, making them some of the longest-living fishes on Earth.

TOP: *Neither wolf nor eel, this creature's strong jaws crunch through the toughest crab shells.*

ABOVE: *Often sold as "rock cod" or "red snapper," rockfishes can't keep up with demand—some populations have declined by 98% since 1970 due to overfishing and habitat loss. Wise fishery management and creating marine protected areas can help their populations recover.*

ABOVE: *Sculpins hug the rubble in the small display with an acrylic top in this gallery, their mottled bodies blending with the background.*
LEFT: *A sheep crab relies on heavy, jointed armor to protect itself from predators.*

Though once called "devilfish" and thought to be ferocious, octopuses are shy, and pose little danger to divers, fishermen or swimmers.

HERE AND GONE

Red rockfish nearly disappear in the dark waters of the deep reef.

STRONG JAWS

A wolf-eel can bite right through a sea urchin.

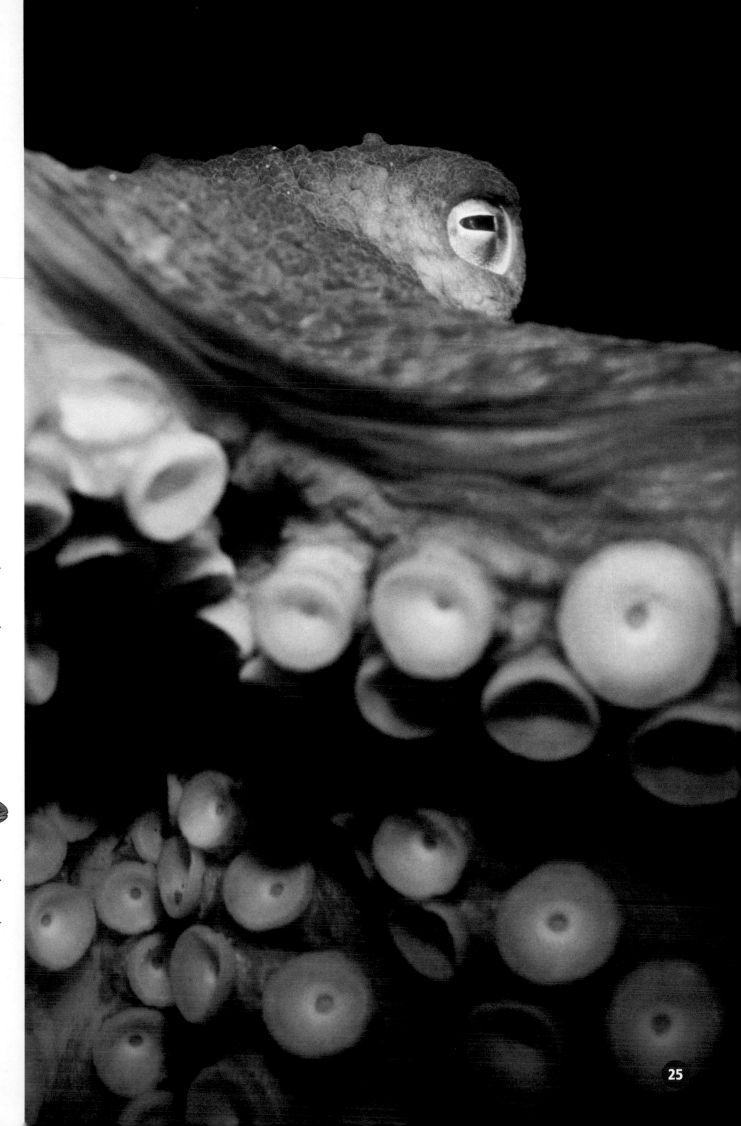

RIGHT: An octopus's eight tentacles are lined with suckers that can "taste" sweet, sour or bitter, or feel if something is rough or smooth.

Monterey Bay Habitats

… inhabitants of the watery element were made for the wise to contemplate, and fools to pass by without consideration. —IZAAK WALTON

There's much to contemplate in the 90-foot-long, 326-gallon Monterey Bay Habitats exhibit, which is really five exhibits in one. Animals swim from open waters over deep reefs, past shale reefs, over a sandy seafloor to 30-year-old wharf pilings from the harbor in this realistic slice of habitats in the bay.

Large sharks, bat rays, salmon, halibut, giant sea bass and many other fishes roam just inches away. Those aren't penguins paddling on the surface or diving and swimming under water, they're really common murres that were rescued from an oil spill along the coast.

Larger animals clad in wetsuits are volunteer divers who join exhibit residents three times a week to clean windows, always keeping an eye on the circling sharks. Don't worry, there are plenty of hiding places for people and fishes to escape if the sharks get too curious.

Bubble windows peer into the exhibit on the aquarium's main floor. Up on the second floor, an overlook gives a peek behind the scenes, and really shows the exhibit's unique hourglass shape, which gives large, constantly swimming sharks the long, straight glide path they need.

ABOVE: *Bubble-shaped viewing windows offer an intriguing perspective on the deep reefs.*

LEFT: *Seven-inch-thick acrylic windows provide a series of broad vistas into the exhibit.*

Special identification chips are tucked under the skin of large sharks to help aquarists keep track of them with a scanner, and note their growth and health.

Sharks, like this horn shark, are efficient predators beautifully adapted to the sea.

A swell shark hatches from a protective pouch on the seafloor.

EMMA

A sevengill shark named Emma grew over nine feet long, so she was released back to the sea.

Bat rays seem to flap their "wings" as they "fly" through the water.

RIGHT: *Reaching the size of a platter, the sunflower star is so fast and voracious, other animals scramble out of the way when they sense its approach.*

Sandy Seafloor

Seek the treasures of the seafloor, these flatlands are home to living gems.

At first glance, the sandy seafloor seems barren. But dig deeper. Hidden treasure—a richness of life—lies buried in the open underwater plains.

Here, waving arms point out the homes of the stars. Piles of brittle stars wave their flexible arms in the water to snare passing bits of food.

Quick-change artists, flatfishes match their color to their background. Suddenly, a bit of seafloor swims off in search of lunch. When the flatfish on the lighter background swim over to the darker side, they disappear as they quickly blend in.

A hidden jewel lies within the egg case on exhibit. Life stirs as the tiny skate or shark wriggles inside its protective, fluid-filled home, getting nourishment from its yolk sac until it's large enough to "hatch."

Anemones root their tubes deep in the sand.

ABOVE: *Sand dollars stand on edge, half-wedged into sandy pockets, and trap bits of food or grab small prey drifting by on the currents.*

RIGHT: *Hermit crabs don't need to dig in. Their armored shells protect them as they scuttle across open, sandy plains.*

ALTERNATIVE LIFESTYLES

Flatfishes start out life looking like other fishes, but early on, one eye migrates to the other side, and they take up life on the seafloor.

Flatfishes hide where there's no place to hide by lying low and blending in, with only their eyes giving them away.

The big-eyed skate deceives with false eyes on its fins.

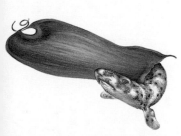

Beachcombers call these egg cases "mermaid's purses" when they wash ashore. Some sharks and rays lay bundles of these leathery egg cases on the seafloor, where the tendrils hold them fast to fixed objects.

RIGHT: *With feathery "branches," sea pens gather food that brushes by in the currents.*

Shale Reef

Where clams dig the caves, all kinds of characters move in.

The hidden world of the shale reef comes to life for those who pause in this quiet corner of the aquarium. Actual shale reef, millions of years old, was brought up from the depths of the bay along with its shy inhabitants snug in their tunnels.

Clams and date mussels burrow for years through the soft shale reefs, opening up new territory for other tunnel dwellers. Some holes contain clams still at work, their siphons drawing in food and oxygen.

Vacant tunnels don't stay empty for long. More than a hundred animals call this bustling reef home. Tiny fringeheads dart from a round burrow amid the waving arms of brittle stars.

Nearby, the crackling "static" of thousands of snapping shrimp draws the curious to explore. These "gunmen" of the sea stun their prey with percussion from their massive claws.

A vermilion rockfish is also called a "rockcod" or a "red snapper," but it's neither cod nor snapper.

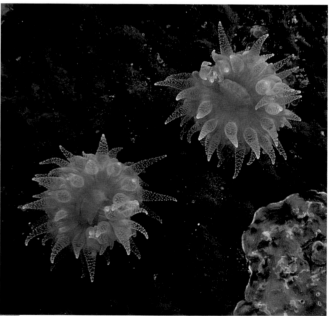

ABOVE: *Creatures crowd the shale's surface in a living tapestry of cobalt-blue sponges, vivid orange cup corals, and bright pink coralline algae, and delicate anemones.*

LEFT: *A shale reef is a bustling community of fishes, sponges, cup corals, worms and crustaceans. This fragile environment, like other marine communities, is at risk from pollutants like motor oil poured down drains or on the ground, which ends up in rivers, lakes and seas. The toxic effects on ocean animals can linger for years.*

For more about shale reefs, visit our web site (www.montereybayaquarium.org) or pick up the aquarium's *Field Guide to the Monterey Bay Aquarium* or *A Natural History of the Monterey Bay National Marine Sanctuary.*

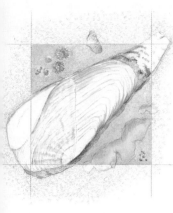

SHALE

Shale reefs are made from the glassy shells of countless one-celled plants that rained down onto the seabed and, over time, were compressed into rock called shale.

A sea lemon grazes on the reef's rich feast.

Lacy tentacles of sea cucumbers spread from caves.

The carnivorous chiton is no larger than a peanut.

RIGHT: *Floating magnifiers reveal the hidden world of a shale reef and the reef creature's innermost secrets.*

31

Wharf

Cannery Row…is a poem, a stink, a grating noise, a quality of light, a tone, a habit, a nostalgia, a dream.

—JOHN STEINBECK

In the Wharf gallery, visitors feel like they're walking below a seaside wharf as they weave among the pilings that reach from floor to ceiling. Though the wharf's not a natural habitat, many animals find it the perfect place to settle down. The water's calm, and food comes in on the tide—or from above, when fishermen dump fish scraps after their catch of the day.

Hungry perches swarm around the pilings, picking at the feast they find there—like barnacles, snails, worms and small crabs. Barnacles compete for space with all the other animals crowding onto pilings, arranging themselves in zones from top to bottom.

Pilings, nooks and crannies aren't the only places animals live under the wharf. Castoff junk provides hiding places for many creatures. It's still no excuse for littering.

Before leaving the wharf, grab a seat at the counter in the Real-Cost Cafe and choose among seafood dishes listed on an interactive menu. Each choice prompts a different interaction with the waiter, waitress and chef via a video screen, letting you know whether your order is sustainable or not. As it turns out, everyone has a role to play in ensuring healthy oceans.

TOP RIGHT: *Under the wharf can be a junky world, as one exhibit shows. Litter may offer a new home here and there, but it's still just pollution.*

RIGHT: *Have a seat at the Real-Cost Cafe exhibit. Instead of a meal, visitors get an entertaining lesson about the hidden costs of ordering canned tuna or Chilean sea bass.*

DON'T SPLASH YOUR TRASH

You can protect wharf animals—
along with seals, sea turtles,
dolphins and diving birds—
by packing your trash after
a day on the wharf.

*On thickly encrusted wharf pilings,
a green anemone competes for
space with different anemones,
barnacles, tunicates and other
sea life.*

PIER PRESSURE IS HEAVY

Many animals seek out a home on
wharf pilings. Few plants grow
here, and food comes in with the
tide or falls as scraps from the
wharf above.

33

Coastal Wetland to Sandy Shore

But in the estuary as in most of nature, the visible is but a shallow footprint of a larger and more elusive truth. —STEWART T. SCHULTZ

Follow the wooden walkway past the Nature Center through the Coastal Wetland to the Sandy Shore and discover life from one of the largest coastal estuaries in the state right in the heart of Monterey Bay—Elkhorn Slough.

Sheltered from the surf by dunes, these wetlands are a quiet world of winding channels, wide salt marshes and mudflats that emerge or disappear with ocean tides. Each part harbors wildlife: birds above, fishes in the water, burrowers under the mud.

Visitors travel through several habitats, from tidal channel to eelgrass mudflats to marsh and over the sand beaches to the wave-swept shores, without even getting wet!

Along the way, peer through a periscope at the bat ray pool for a bat ray's view, or touch one as it glides by.

Nearby, sandpipers forage among the dunes abloom with native plants, and avocets and black-necked stilts stride the shore probing for food. A hidden machine triggers small waves that lap on shore. Washed-up seaweed thrown on the beach lets the birds pick through for insects, as they would in the wild.

An avocet (left) and a black-necked stilt roam the beach in the aviary, which also serves as a refuge for rescued birds that won't survive if released.

Tread lightly when you visit the beaches and dunes; don't uproot the plants or disturb their homes. In this fragile ecosystem, the damage we do in a day can take years to recover.

Aquarium employees are helping to restore Elkhorn Slough by planting native grasses on abandoned farmlands bordering the wetlands.

BIRD FEED

The aquarium buys 260,000 crickets a year to feed the birds in the aviary.

Shovelnose guitarfish, leopard sharks and other fishes ride the surge, or lie in wait close to shore.

Nearly all of the birds in the aviary have been rescued from the wild.

Heavy roots help California poppies hold their ground in the sand.

RIGHT: *The new Ocean's Edge galleries include a greatly expanded Coastal Aviary exhibit. Leopard sharks and bat rays swim by on one side, while a wave-lapped beach and wetlands habitat lie on the other.*

Rocky Shore

At land's end, the tide rushes in, sweeping over the sea plants and animals that embroider the shore. Distinct bands of life mark rocky coasts.

From the high and dry rocks—wetted only by sea spray and occasional waves—to lush rocks exposed by only the lowest tides, each zone on the rocky coast has its own cast of characters.

In the Rocky Shore gallery, the secret lives of those who live on the bay's edge are revealed for all to see. A shy monkeyface eel stares back from among the rocks. Nearby, the tide pool video camera brings a brilliant cast to the big screen.

It's a world where crushing waves and swirling currents govern who lives where, or is swept away, or gets pounded into oblivion.

Surfperches, at home in the perpetual motion of surge channels, turn to face currents created with a hand-turned crank. Another crank sets up food-rich currents that bring out a barnacle's feathery legs, and teases anemones to open like flowers.

Just around the corner, the waves come swooshing in and everybody hangs on for dear life, or gets carried out to sea.

Ed Ricketts, whose work inspired the founders of the aquarium, co-authored the beloved classic, Between Pacific Tides.

TOP: *Sea stars eat by extending their stomachs onto their prey and dissolving it with strong enzymes.*

ABOVE: *A lined shore crab seeks protection under the tentacles of a green anemone, but could become a meal itself.*

Tidepool sculpins look like rocks by lying very still.

HEADSTANDS

Barnacles stand on their heads within their hard cases, and wave their feathery legs in the currents to catch tiny plankton.

The vivid colors and patterns of nudibranchs warn predators of bad taste.

A crab's hard shell protects it from predators, but must be shed so the crab can grow.

RIGHT: *Twice each day the tide ebbs, unveiling bat stars and other survivors of the surf zone.*

Waves and Tides

The tides are in our veins.

–ROBINSON JEFFERS

On the rocky edge of the bay, waves and tides rule life along the crowded shores, as they do in the lively wave crash and tide pool exhibits.

Visitors experience firsthand the turbulence of the rocky shore when waves crash right overhead in the wave-crash tunnel. Sea life in this fast lane survives by hanging on or laying low when waves that blast everything in their path hit with enough force to throw boulders. Plants hold on and flex with the flow, shore crabs hide in crevices and flat sea stars cling with strong tube feet.

As the waves roll in, the tides rise and fall twice a day in the bay, but in here, they ebb and flow four times. At low tide, tide pools abound with life, from soft sea cucumbers to spiny sea urchins.

In the Rocky Shore Touch Pool, volunteer guides show how to touch these animals carefully, and offer the proper etiquette for visiting tide pools on your own. What to remember? Step cautiously and touch gently, or better yet, just look.

ABOVE: *Volunteer guides connect people and animals at the Touch Pool, leaving them with a greater respect and appreciation for life along the rocky shore.*

RIGHT: *Volunteers help students become young discoverers*

A bat star clings to rocks with hundreds of strong suction-cup tube feet.

In the summer, aquarium staff introduce visitors of all ages to the marine life in the bay.

HIGH TIDE

The tidal fluctuation in the bay is about six feet, and the highest tide nearly submerges the outer rocks of the Great Tide Pool.

I spin on the circle
of wave upon wave
of the sea.

PABLO NERUDA

TIDE POOL

The Great Tide Pool is named after one of Ed Ricketts' favorite tide pools, near Point Pinos in Pacific Grove.

RIGHT: *The action comes in waves at the Wave Crash exhibit. Every 30 seconds, water crashes down into the outdoor tide pools . . . and right over the heads of surprised guests.*

Sea Otters

What looks like an enchanting and cuddly creature . . . is actually a highly specialized marine mammal, uniquely adapted for living in a wet, cold and harsh marine world. —MARIANNE RIEDMAN

ABOVE: *Otters have sharp teeth for eating crabs, urchins, clams and other invertebrates. Exhibit otters never learned how to forage in the wild, and would have starved had they not been rescued.*

The lively sea otters on exhibit came to the aquarium as rescued pups, possibly separated from their mothers by heavy surf. They never learned the hunting skills they'd need in the wild, and seem quite at home in their exhibit, where they romp, tumble, wrestle and interact like otters in the bay.

It looks like fun but all of that rubbing and rolling is vital: keeping their fur clean and fluffy makes it waterproof and helps the otters stay warm in the cold water. Sea otters have the thickest fur in the world—up to one million hairs per square inch.

The aquarium otters eat chopped surf clams, fish fillets, squid and whole shrimp. Each otter gets about 15 percent of its body weight in seafood a day, spaced out over four feedings. For a treat, they get crabs to crunch. Putting food into toys stimulates the otter's natural behaviors of pounding and working to get food out of shells. The otters also forage at submerged feeder ports, which encourages them to dive for food like they would in the wild. It costs up to $12,000 a year to feed just one otter.

Twice a month, the otters crawl onto a scale so aquarists know just how much food they need to maintain proper weight. Once a week, staff check each otter's eyes, mouth and body, and listen to their hearts with a stethoscope.

LEFT: *Staff teach the otters voice and hand signals and condition them to hold still for stress-free health exams.*

California sea otters spend most of their life at sea near kelp forests.

Second-floor viewing windows let visitors watch sea otters at the surface, while first-floor windows give an underwater view of the otters in their 55,000-gallon exhibit.

For more about sea otters, pick up our natural history book, *Sea Otters,* or visit our web site (www.montereybayaquarium.org).

Holding its paws out of the cold water helps the sea otter regulate its 100° F body temperature, a tough task in chilly 35° F– 60° F sea water.

Saving Sea Otters

If the tap-tapping of the sea otter is to remain . . . along our shores, it will demand more than foresight. It will require vision.

—MARGARET WENTWORTH OWINGS

Southern sea otters once ranged from Baja California to the Pacific Northwest. Today, they're found only on California's Central Coast, at a fraction of their historic numbers. The population is growing slowly, when it grows at all.

Sea otters are facing threats that weren't a concern when they were placed on the endangered species list in 1977. Disease and parasites, possibly linked to coastal pollution, take a heavy toll. The risk of a major oil spill remains a serious threat.

Fortunately, a new federal recovery plan for California's sea otters is designed to help the species flourish, and the aquarium has a key role in it. With 20 years of leadership in sea otter conservation efforts, our Sea Otter Research and Conservation program is working with scientists at the University of California, Santa Cruz, to discover why California's threatened otter population is in crisis.

We'll continue to return rescued animals to the wild that have the greatest chance to help the population recover, especially stranded females of breeding age. We're also studying otters in the wild, and working with others across the country to share information with visitors and policy makers about the plight of sea otters and how we can all help them survive.

Sea otters are in trouble, because they can only do as well as the ecosystem that supports them. The aquarium's new Center for the Future of the Oceans is working at the state, federal and international levels to promote sound ocean policy. Protecting our coastal waters will ensure California sea otters have a future.

We've taken part in sea otter studies that monitor population health, measure how much energy otters expend finding food, determine how otters use their sense of smell to find food, and document how well young otters survive in the wild after they're weaned from their mothers.

ABOVE: *One Sea Otter Research and Conservation Program project matches orphaned sea otter pups with female otters at the aquarium that act as surrogate mothers.*

LEFT: *Sea otters that come into the aquarium because they are unable to survive on their own receive state-of-the-art veterinary care from our sea otter staff.*

Purple sea urchins are a favorite meal for otters.

While different sea otters may have different tastes, their menu in the wild is a big one. Decorator crabs (above) and squid (below) are on it.

WE STILL HAVE A LOT TO LEARN

To help southern sea otters survive for generations to come, scientists must learn why the population is growing so slowly. To find out how you can help, visit our web site at www.montereybayaquarium.org

Once up to 20,000 southern sea otters lived along the Pacific Coast, but today there are fewer than 3,000.

43

Marine Mammals

To see marine mammals, look to the sea with patience and sharp eyes. But to learn their stories, look to the Marine Mammals gallery.

Once a year, the ocean nomads—elephant seals—head to Año Nuevo's protected shores to breed in crowded rookeries.

From blue whales, the largest animal ever to live on Earth, to sea lions cavorting through the waves, to pods of dolphins riding the bow wave of a fishing boat, the parade of marine mammals along the shore is never-ending.

The parade wends its way overhead into the Marine Mammals gallery in the life-like, life-size fiberglass models swimming overhead. A 43-foot, barnacle-encrusted gray whale mother guards her 22-foot calf from their natural enemies, the orcas swimming above the Information Desk.

Dolphins, porpoises and other marine mammals from the bay crowd the air above, while graphics and videos tell their tales and reveal why the bay is a haven for so many species.

Other than sea otters, no marine mammals live in the aquarium. But they're here every day. At times, scores of sea lions pack the breakwater. Their hoarse barking fills the air when passing boats rouse them.

A school of Pacific white-sided dolphins swims up a flight of stairs and the escalator to the Outer Bay galleries. They're heading out to sea!

Sea lions haul out on buoys and channel markers in the bay.

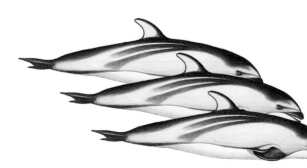

White-sided dolphins swim in herds of thousands, and form close-knit groups.

Gray whales once lived in the North Atlantic, where they are now extinct. Protected by law, the population along the west coast of America has made a comeback.

For more about marine mammals, pick up the natural history books, *Gray Whales*, and *Seals and Sea Lions* or visit www.montereybayaquarium.org.

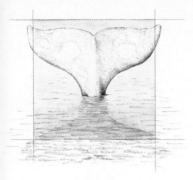

ROOKERIES

Sea lions haul out in crowded rookeries, while harbor seals seek more secluded beaches or rocks.

Scan the bay waters for the shy, bobbing heads of harbor seals or their sausage-shaped bodies perched on the rocks.

LONG-DISTANCE SWIMMERS

Gray whales migrate from their feeding grounds on the Bering Sea to nursery lagoons in Baja California, a roundtrip journey of 12,000 miles a year!

Gray whales stay near the coast on their long journeys and can be seen in Monterey Bay from December through March.

RIGHT: *The best place to see humpback whales and other whales and dolphins is in their natural habitat, out on Monterey Bay.*

Beyond the tide pools and kelp forests, beyond the shallow waters pressed close against the shores, lies another world . . . the outer bay.

The Outer Bay

The outer bay is a world of constant motion with no visible walls and no place to hide.

These restless waters are home to translucent, pulsing jellies and sleek, muscular fishes, pastures of microscopic plankton and roaming sharks and sea turtles.

The Outer Bay galleries capture the feeling of being suspended in the middle of open water 60 miles offshore, far above the seafloor. Overhead, thousands of swirling, silvery anchovies swim in a 36-foot by 26-foot oval exhibit, 65 feet in circumference and holding 15,000 gallons of water.

But much of the life in this blue realm drifts by, too tiny, too transparent to see. In the Tiny Drifters gallery, a drop of sea water is swimming with magical life: young crabs in spiked disguise, armored animals, and tiny plants. Microscopes reveal fantastical larval forms.

Not all drifters are small. In the Drifters gallery, the larger, elegant jellies are a study of grace and beauty as they gently pulse through the water.

Other life looms larger. The Outer Bay exhibit houses a million-gallon indoor ocean that carries you to the very heart of the outer bay during a warm El Niño pattern. Schools of streamlined bonito speed past. Yellowfin tuna power their way through the water. Sea turtles, visitors from the tropics, cruise lazily.

In the Swimmers gallery, mackerel glide effortlessly in the open water. Schooling helps open-ocean fishes avoid predators, like sharks. Nearby, a model of a sleek blue shark pursues a school of Pacific mackerel spiraling toward the Exploring the Outer Bay gallery, where a mix of live exhibits, videos and interactive displays explores the open ocean and its inhabitants in more depth.

ABOVE: *Sea nettles pulse and drift in an exhibit specially designed to keep them floating freely.*

LEFT: *Odd-looking ocean sunfish slowly flap by the window in the Outer Bay exhibit.*

How many anchovies swim in this donut-shaped exhibit? Hint: it changes all the time, but 3,000 is a pretty good guess.

For more about the outer bay, pick up the *Natural History of the Monterey Bay National Marine Sanctuary,* or visit our web site www.montereybayaquarium.org.

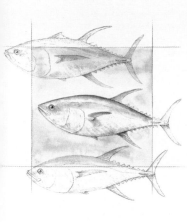

EL NIÑO

The Outer Bay exhibit is warmed to 68˚F to mimic an El Niño pattern in the open ocean.

Comb jellies dazzle and beguile by shimmering with iridescent rainbows of refracted light.

OUTER BAY WINDOW

The acrylic Outer Bay window weighs 78,000 pounds and is 54 feet long, 15 feet tall and 13 inches thick. Five panels were fused together to create a seamless view.

RIGHT: *Cousin to the yellowfin here, the Pacific bluefin tuna is the only unregulated bluefin fishery in the world. The demand for this tuna has grown as stocks of its Atlantic cousin dwindle.*

Jellies & Other Drifters

Transparent. Translucent. Transcendent. Bell and tentacles. Nothing hidden. A gelatinous body of nerves. Pulsating. Throbbing. Drifting. A jelly is more verb than noun. —TERRY TEMPEST WILLIAMS.

Drifting silently in a dreamlike, turquoise-blue world, a sea nettle tangles its long tentacles with another graceful jelly in the mesmerizing Drifters gallery. Nearby, a comb jelly pulses with rainbow bands of light as it zips through the water in search of food. Jellies come in all shapes and sizes, from the tiniest of Tinkerbells to giants more than 100 feet long.

Simple in appearance, these and other jellies live shrouded in mystery. But just how they move through the water and catch other animals comes to light at the nine-foot-long model around the corner.

They may seem spun of gossamer and dreams, but jellies are the dominant predators on Earth, and sweep the seas, capturing other animals in their stinging tentacles.

In these large exhibits, ocean-going species like egg-yolk jellies seem right at home in 10-foot-long exhibits lit to show off their beauty. The secret: special tanks designed here, called "kreisels," which keep them from hitting hard walls or corners. You'd never know the tanks are really only 18 inches deep—they look like they go on forever.

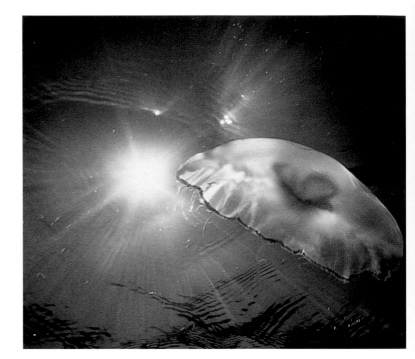

Jellies go with the flow, drifting where the currents take them. The trash thrown in the ocean floats along with the jellies, changing an environment we hardly know anything about.

A crystal jelly is transparent, it almost hides right out in the open.

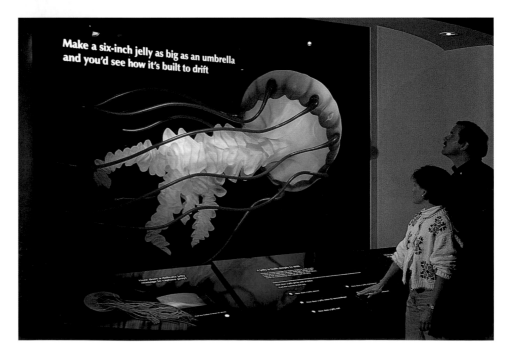

Make a six-inch jelly as big as an umbrella and you'd see how it's built to drift

A larger-than-life jelly model lights up with jelly lore.

 For more about jellies, visit www.montereybayaquarium.org, or pick up the aquarium's book, *Jellies: Living Art.*

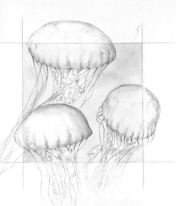

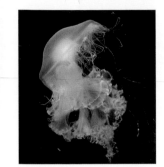

With long tentacles, the egg-yolk jelly captures and eats other jellies.

JELLIES

Jellies are 95 percent water!

Comb jellies flash rainbows of refracted light as they move in search of other jellies to eat.

NETTLES

Jellies belong to a group of animals whose name means "nettle" in Greek.

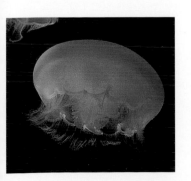

For part of its life, a moon jelly lives attached to the seafloor until it becomes a pulsing, free-floating adult.

The sea nettle display holds 2,000 gallons of water, weighs 13 tons and is the largest exhibit of its kind in the world.

Open Waters

. . . a window onto the endless, mysterious ocean world that lies beyond the narrow strand of coastal habitats. The outer bay is full of drama.

The stunning one-million-gallon Outer Bay exhibit is home to the largest and most diverse community of open-ocean animals to be found in any aquarium, and the only permanent exhibit of tuna in America.

Through one of the largest windows on Earth, the view looks limitless as oceanic whitetip, soupfin and hammerhead sharks circle just inches away. Wary schools of yellowfin and bluefin tuna and bonito keep an eye on the sharks, as do the California barracuda, pilotfish and dolphinfish. There's plenty of room to roam in this 90-foot-long, 35-foot-deep exhibit, one of the tallest aquarium exhibits in the world.

Speedy tunas and barracudas eat 1,100 pounds of squid, smelt and vitamin-rich gelatin a week. The slower-moving sea turtles and sunfish get fed by hand.

Nearby, next to the wall of windows with the magnificent bay view, the Ocean Travelers gallery introduces the stories of pelicans, sea turtles, tunas and many other species that are seasonal residents of the bay. The fate of these animals depends on the health of Monterey Bay and the oceans of the world through which they journey. Trace their migration routes, or learn what action will help protect ocean habitats.

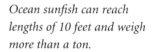

Ocean sunfish can reach lengths of 10 feet and weigh more than a ton.

From September 2004 to March 2005, the first white shark ever to thrive outside of the wild lived in the Outer Bay exhibit. She grew from 5 feet long and 62 pounds to 6 feet four inches and 162 pounds before she was tagged and successfully released.

Every species of sea turtle, like this green sea turtle, is endangered throughout the world's oceans, due to drowning in fishing nets and real estate development on their nesting beaches.

Conserving Vanishing Wildlife

Conservation of ocean wildlife is the aquarium's top priority.

Blink your eyes and they're gone. Sleek-bodied, powerful tuna tuck their fins into grooves on their sides and streak by the viewing window in the Vanishing Wildlife: Saving Tunas, Turtles and Sharks gallery. They're one of the fastest fish in the sea.

The stunning view into the million-gallon Outer Bay exhibit is slanted at a 60-degree angle above your head, giving a rare look up into schools of tuna, circling sharks and gliding sea turtles. The rest of the gallery paints a sobering view of the growing demand for seafood and of the destructive fishing practices that threaten ocean wildlife.

Sharks and other ocean pelagics are in trouble worldwide. We launched a white shark research program in 2002, and for the first time ever, exhibited a young white shark that thrived for more than six months before she was tagged and returned to the wild in March 2005. Two key results of this project have been better-informed shark conservation policy and a higher public awareness of the plight of all shark species.

The aquarium is partnering with Stanford University's Hopkins Marine Station next door on a new and greatly expanded California white shark research initiative to discover where white sharks go and why, where pups are born and critical information about their basic physiology. Armed with that knowledge, we can take steps to create more informed commercial fishing practices that protect this threatened and misunderstood top predator.

The aquarium is also partnering with researchers around the world to study sharks, tuna and other ocean predators. Together with Stanford University, we fund and operate the Tuna Research and Conservation Center (TRCC), the world's leading tuna research center.

TRCC researchers are also tagging sharks in the North Pacific as part of a multi-year, multi-institution collaboration called Tagging of Pacific Pelagics (TOPP). TOPP brings together scientists from all over the world to study the migration patterns of large, open-ocean animals, like white sharks, bluefin tuna, elephant seals, albatrosses, sea turtles, whales and other marine species in the North Pacific Ocean.

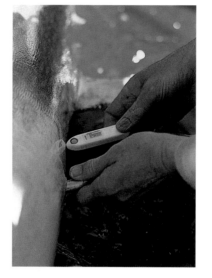

Scientists collaborate with sport fishermen through the Tag-A-Giant program.

TRCC scientists are leaders in a program to tag open ocean animals in the Pacific basin as part of a first-ever global Census of Marine Life.

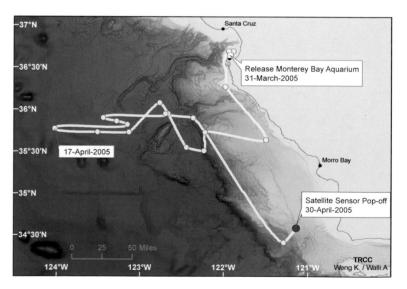

Before releasing her, researchers placed a satellite tag on the first white shark ever to do well on exhibit. In the 30 days she was tracked, she traveled 100 miles and dove as deep as 820 feet.

More than one hundred million sharks are killed each year, half of them victims of fishing gear seeking other species.

Scientists sail the high seas to tag tuna.

Yellowfin and other tunas are nomads of the sea, long-distance migrators that move up to 100 miles a day across tropical and temperate ocean basins.

Tagging tuna on the high seas takes skill and speed.

RIGHT: *Scientists tag individual tuna in the wild with micro-processor-equipped data tags, which pop free and beam stored information via satellite to scientists in the lab. A tag on this tuna will reveal where it travels in the world.*

55

Center for the Future of Oceans

We can't sit on the sidelines when the future of the oceans is at stake.

– JULIE PACKARD

Our survival, and that of countless other creatures, depends on healthy oceans. But the world's oceans are at risk, so to turn the tide against the growing threats, the aquarium created the Center for the Future of the Oceans.

The Center embraces all of our conservation policy programs, from marine protected areas to southern sea otters to sustainable seafood choices.

We believe conservation starts at home, so the Center empowers individuals through our Seafood Watch program. Handy wallet cards help you select seafood from sustainable fish and shellfish populations.

The Center also supports comprehensive public policy reform at the state and federal levels, as recommended by the U.S. Commission on Ocean Policy and the independent Pew Oceans Commission. California's landmark Marine Life Protection Act, and the setting aside of marine protected areas where sea life can flourish are a major priority.

Through it all, sound science must come into play. This can only happen if the public, policymakers and media understand the science behind the problems and the solutions. That's the idea behind the Communication Partnership for Science and the Sea (COMPASS), our initiative to raise awareness of marine conservation science and communicate that knowledge to policy makers, the public and the media.

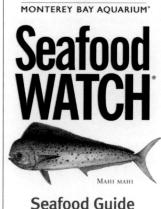

Let our Seafood Watch pocket guide help you make ocean-friendly choices in restaurants and markets. When you select seafood from the Best Choices list, you'll help make the future brighter for generations of sea life— and seafood lovers—to come. To get your own copy, visit our website at www.monterey bayaquarium.org

Sea otters and snowy plovers are just two examples of wildlife that urgently need the kinds of benefits well-designed marine protected areas can provide.

A legacy of healthy oceans is the ultimate goal for the Center for the Future of the Oceans. Implementing sound, science-based ocean policy will be one key to that.

Family Fun

Our children are the future stewards for the oceans.

Children are the future and our best hope for restoring healthy oceans, so we've created a place where children and their families can discover animals in new and exciting ways.

In our award-winning Splash Zone galleries, designed especially for families, kids crawl through, climb on, slide down and pop up in more than 30 displays simulating coral reefs and rocky shores.

In the Crowded Coral Reef, children crawl past giant clams through a coral cave and come face-to-face with living jewels from coral seas in kid-size tanks. For the very young ones, there's Coral Cove, with a crawl-on waterbed and soft-foam "baby pond" for infants.

The fun continues over in the Outer Bay galleries. Flippers, Flukes and Fun displays encourage children, and their adult companions, to explore the bay where whales sing, dolphins squeak and elephant seals bellow.

Hands-on learning is a key element of Flippers, Flukes and Fun.

Children learn about the risks of living on the Rocky Shore in "Splash Zone."

Over in the Rough Rocky Shore, kids splash around in the waterplay exhibit while learning how rocky shore creatures hang on to the rocks, or ride the waves.

Children come face to face with living jewels from the coral seas in "Splash Zone."

The South African blackfooted penguins in "Splash Zone," like many penguins, are threatened and need protection from habitat destruction.

Future Ocean Stewards

Our philosophy of inspiring, engaging and empowering people to protect the oceans pervades everything we do . . .

–JULIE PACKARD

The aquarium's commitment to inspiring a constituency who will speak out on behalf of the oceans is the philosophy behind all of our programs that immerse youth and families in the wonders of ocean life on the bay, and behind the scenes.

From summer Aquarium Adventures to the year-long Student Oceanography Club, week-long Young Women in Science and multi-year Teacher Institutes, we're engaging and empowering the next generation of ocean stewards.

Our summer selection of Aquarium Adventures programs offers exciting choices, from supervised surface scuba in Underwater Explorers for kids to a Science Under Sail research expedition on Monterey Bay on our state-of-the-art, 65-foot research sailboat. Or join us on Morning Rounds for a rare opportunity to interact with our exhibit animals as an aquarist would. To discover the history of a street made famous by John Steinbeck, take a gentle stroll along Cannery Row, in a program co-sponsored by the Maritime Museum of Monterey.

Programs in the aquarium's Discovery Labs and tours for more than 80,000 school children every year customize marine science programs for each class's unique needs, and spark a life-long passion for the sea and the creatures that call it home.

The Student Oceanography Club inspires conservation by bringing together students ages 11–17 twice a month, from October to May, to explore ocean diversity through science, art and other disciplines.

ABOVE: *Teachers and school administrators gather at the aquarium each year for experiences in marine science, and spend time in the field, laboratory, aquarium, classroom and online.*

RIGHT: *Besides hands-on science, each Discovery Lab always includes a discussion of the roles students can play in marine conservation.*

Teachers experience research at sea first-hand during the teacher programs that last from one to 20 days.

The aquarium's many programs for kids get them out on the bay, and even in it, to inspire them and motivate them to be an oceans advocate as they grow older.

RIGHT: *Splish, splash! Kids dive into the "Splash Zone," upstairs in the Ocean's Edge galleries, designed especially for families.*

Come cuddle up in a giant clam!

Giant clams can grow to four feet across.

The opportunity to connect with ocean animals and discover what lies beneath the ocean surface is the start of a path toward awareness, commitment and action. It's our ultimate goal to build a constituency for the oceans . . . won't you join us? —JULIE PACKARD

Managing Editor: Michelle McKenzie
Project Managers: Hank Armstrong and Nora L. Deans
Design: Gordon Chun Design
Photo Editors: Nora L. Deans, Michelle McKenzie, Miki Elizondo
Photo Research: Kris Ingram
Writer: Nora L. Deans
Contributing Writers: Hank Armstrong, Eileen Campbell, Alice Cascorbi,
   Ava Ferguson, Melissa Hutchinson, Elizabeth Labor, Ken Peterson,
   Christina Joie Slager, Jenny Sayre Ramberg, Judy Rand, Michael Rigsby,
   Jaci Tomulonis.

Photographs and Illlustrations

Published in the United States by the Monterey Bay Aquarium Foundation,
886 Cannery Row, Monterey, California 93940-1045
www.montereybayaquarium.org

Printed in Hong Kong on recycled paper

ISBN: 1-878244-40-X